Listen, Listen

written by Phillis Gershator
illustrated by Alison Jay

Arabic translation by Wafa' Tarnowska

إسمعْ ، إسمعْ ... ما هذا الصوت؟ انه صوتُ الحشراتِ تغنّي ما حولْ.

Listen, listen ... what's that sound? Insects singing all around!

زِيءْ ، زِيءْ ، خِشْ ، خِشْ ، زِرّْ ، زِرّْ ، فِرّْ ، فِرّْ.

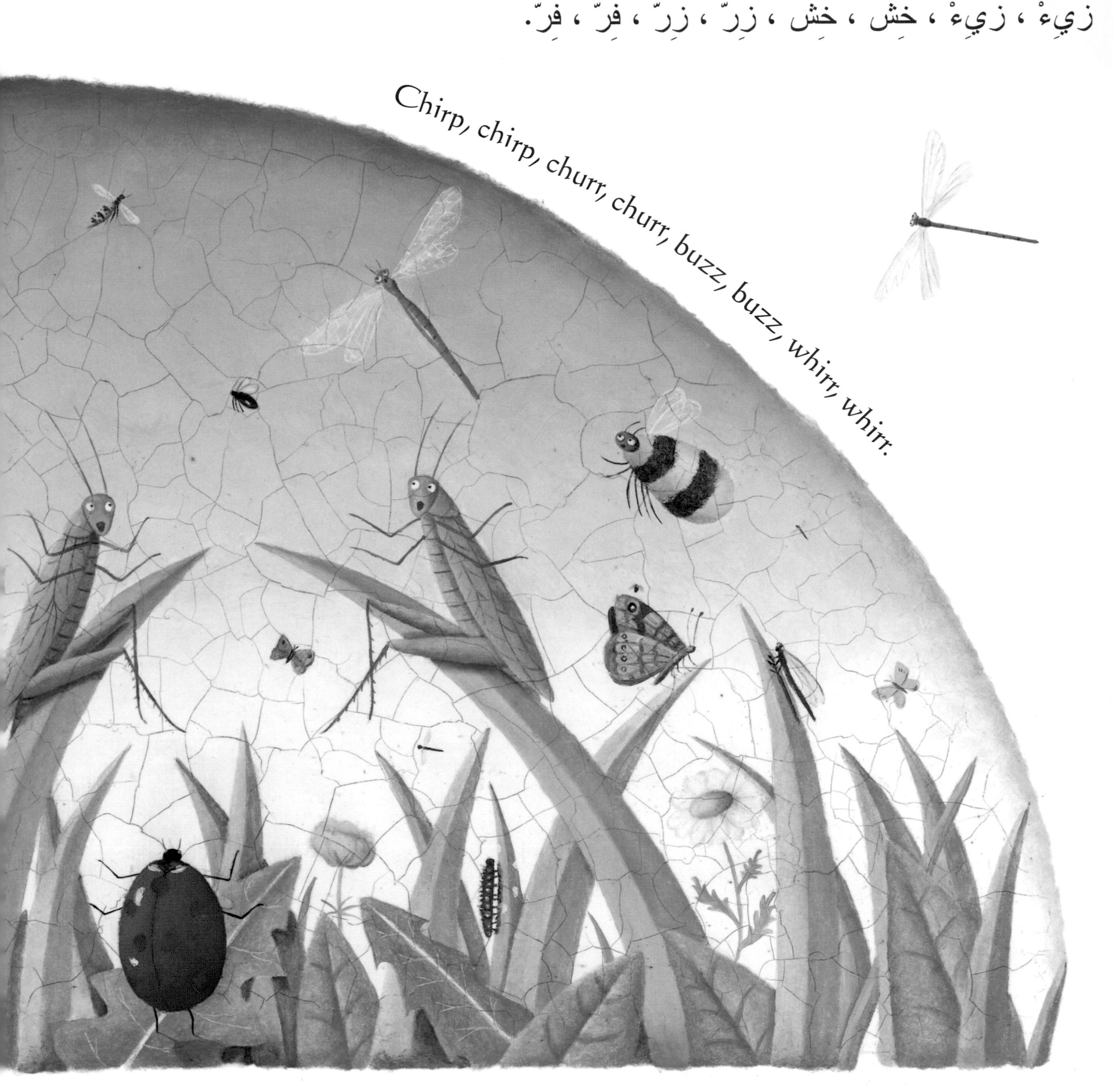

Chirp, chirp, churr, churr, buzz, buzz, whirr, whirr.

أوراقُ الأشجارِ تُخَشْخِشُ والمراجيحُ تَميلْ. رِشّ ، رِشّ ، طَرْطَشَ الأولادُ الماءْ.

Leaves rustle, hammocks sway. Splish, splash, children play.

تسرَحُ السحابْ ، تَجري الكِلابْ. حَرَقَ ، تحرُقُ ، شمسُ الصَّيفِ الخنّاقْ.

Clouds drift, dogs run. Sizzle, sizzle, summer sun.

إسمعْ ، إسمَعْ ... لقد ذهَبَ الصيفْ. ودِّعِ الحشَرات ، فقَدْ حلَّ الخريفْ.

Listen, listen ... summer's gone.
Good-bye insects, autumn's come.

سقَط ، يسِقُطُ ، وقَعَت الاكوازْ. أسرِعْ ، عَجِّلْ ، قَفَزَ السنجابْ.

Plop, plop, acorns drop.
Hurry, scurry, squirrels hop.

نَضَجَ ، يَنْضُجُ ، بسِرعَةٍ اللقطينْ. قَطَفْ ، يُقطفْ ، التُفاحُ والذرةْ اللّينِ.

Pumpkins ripen, quick, quick. Apples, corn - pick, pick.

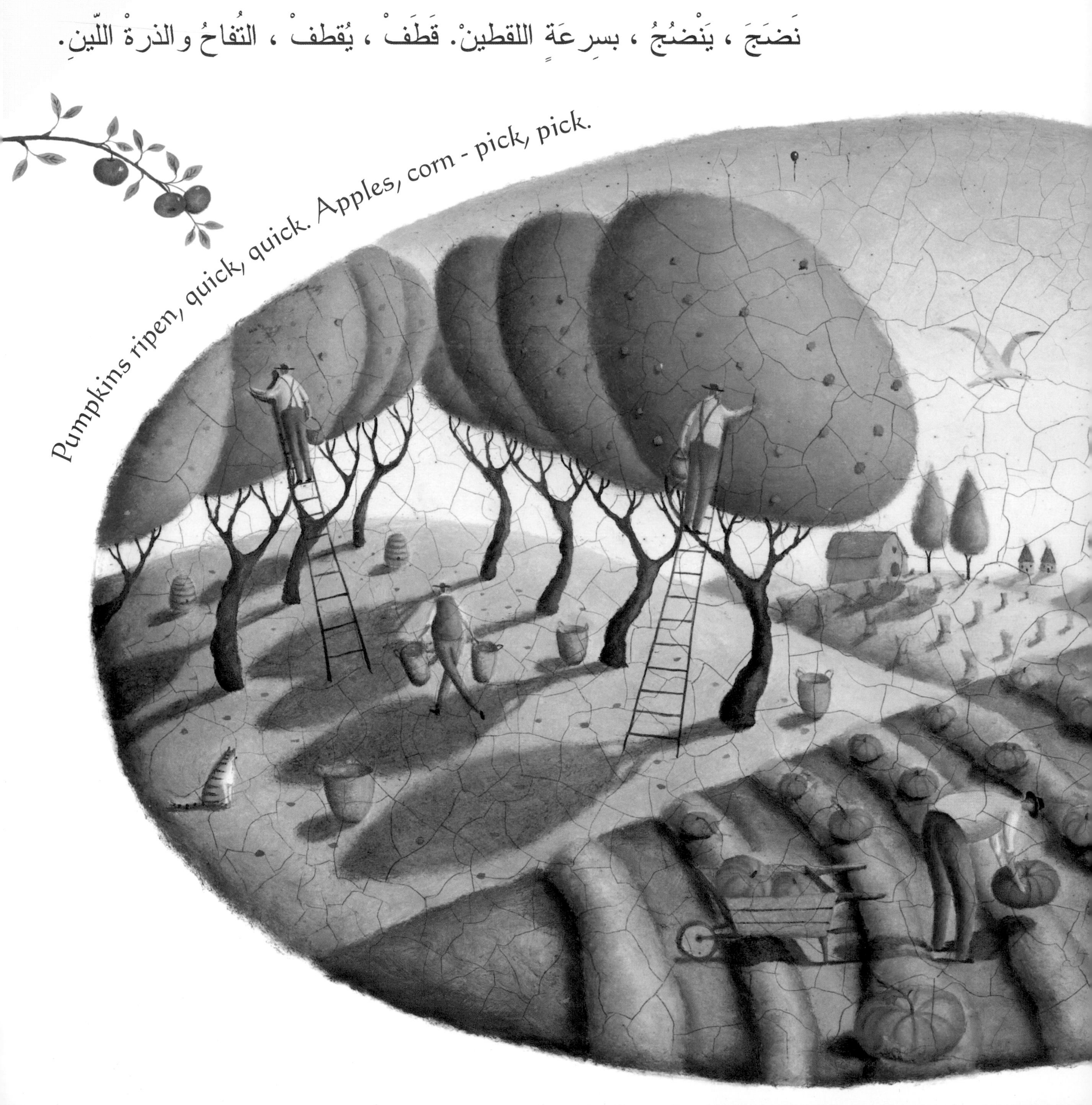

دعَسَ ، يَدْعَسُ ، مَشَى الناسْ. صاحَ ، يصيحُ ، صرخَ النَوَرْسْ.

Crunch, crunch, people walk. Aak, aak, seagulls squawk.

دعا ، يَدْعوا ، نادَت الوزّات. وقَعَ ، تَقَعُ ، هبطَتْ الوَرَقات.

Honk, honk, geese call. Swish, swish, leaves fall.

طارَ ، يطيرُ ، طارَ ت القبّعاتْ. صاحَ ، يَصيحُ ، بكَت البوماتْ.

Whoosh, whoosh, hats fly. Whoo, whoo, owls cry.

إسمَعْ ، إسمَعْ ... ذهَبَ الخريفْ. همسَتْ رقاقاتُ الثلجِ ، "الشتاءُ مَرِحْ."

Listen, listen ... autumn's gone. Snowflakes whisper, "Winter's fun."

شْ ، شْ ، ليلَةٌ تلجّيَةْ. تلمعُ حبّاتُ الثلجِ بيضاءَ زهِيّةْ.

Shhh, shhh, snowy night. Snow sparkles, white, bright.

دَعَسَ ، يدعَسُ ، خطَتْ الاحذيةُ الثقيلةْ. جرَفَ الراشدون الثلجَ ، لعِبَ الأولادْ.

Crunch, crunch, boots clomp. Grown-ups shovel, children romp.

يدورُ المتزلِّجونَ ، يَنزلِقُ المتزحلقونْ. أسْرَعَ ، يُسْرِعُ ، إنزلَقَ ، ينزلِقونْ.

Skaters spin, skiers glide. Zip, zoom, slip, slide.

حُو ، حُو ، حانَ وقتُ الدفىءْ. آهْ ، أو ، لمعَت الشموعْ.

Brrr, brrr, warm-up time. Ooh, aah, candles shine.

نَوّ ، نَوّ ، حدَّقَتْ القِطَطْ. طقطَقَتْ ، فرقَعَتْ ، النارُ إشتعَلَتْ.

Purr, purr, cats gaze. Crackle, crackle, fires blaze.

إسمَعْ ، إسمَعْ ... رحلَ الشتاءْ. زَقْزقَت العصافيرْ ، "أطلَّت الشمسْ!"

Listen, listen ... winter's gone. Finches whistle, "Here's the sun!"

عَلَتْ ، تَعلو ، أورقَتْ البصلاتْ. نبَتَتِ الأوراق ، صاحت الزهراتْ.

Pop, pop, bulbs sprout. Leaves grow, flowers shout.

كسَرَ ، يكسُرُ ، الصيصانُ البَيضْ. زقْزَقَ ، يزقزِقُ ، حَفَرَ الدجاجُ الأرضْ.

Crick, crack, babies hatch. Peep, peep, chickens scratch.

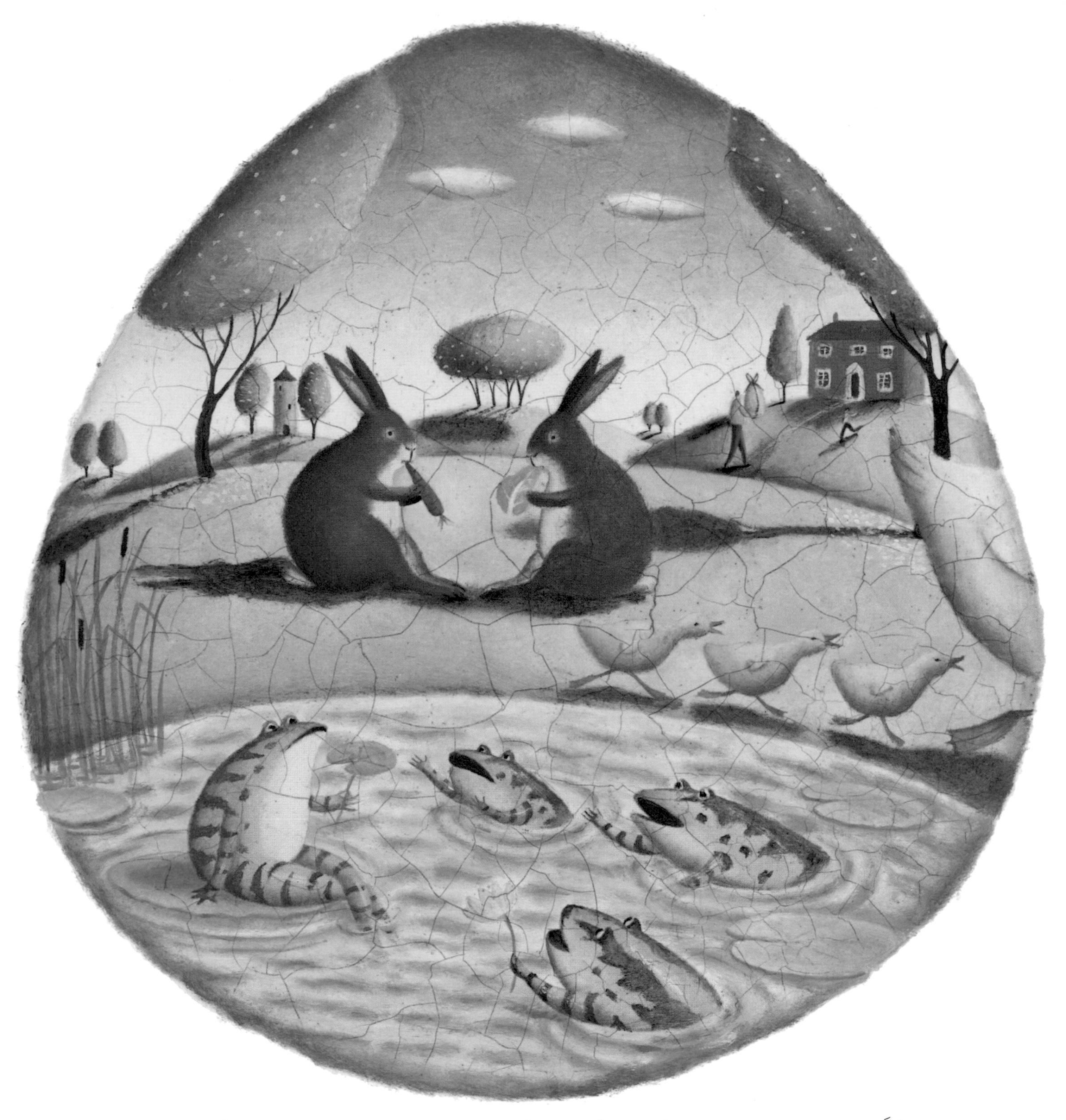

نَقَّت الضفادعُ ، قاقَ البطْ. قَرشَت الارانِبُ ، أَكلَتِ العُشْبْ.

Frogs croak, ducklings quack. Munch, munch, rabbits snack.

هطَلَ المطَرُ ، نَقَرَ ، يَنْقَرُ. تجمَّعَ الدوري ، دَرْدَشَ ، وثرثرْ.

Rains fall, pitter, patter. Sparrows gather, chitter, chatter.

إسمع ، إسمَع ... لقد ذهَبَ الربيع. وحلَّ بعدَهُ فصلٌ آخَرْ.

Listen, listen ... spring is gone. Another season has begun.

في الهواءِ ، على الأرضِ ، ليلاً ونهارْ – ما هذا الصوتْ؟

In the air, on the ground, night and day - what's that sound?

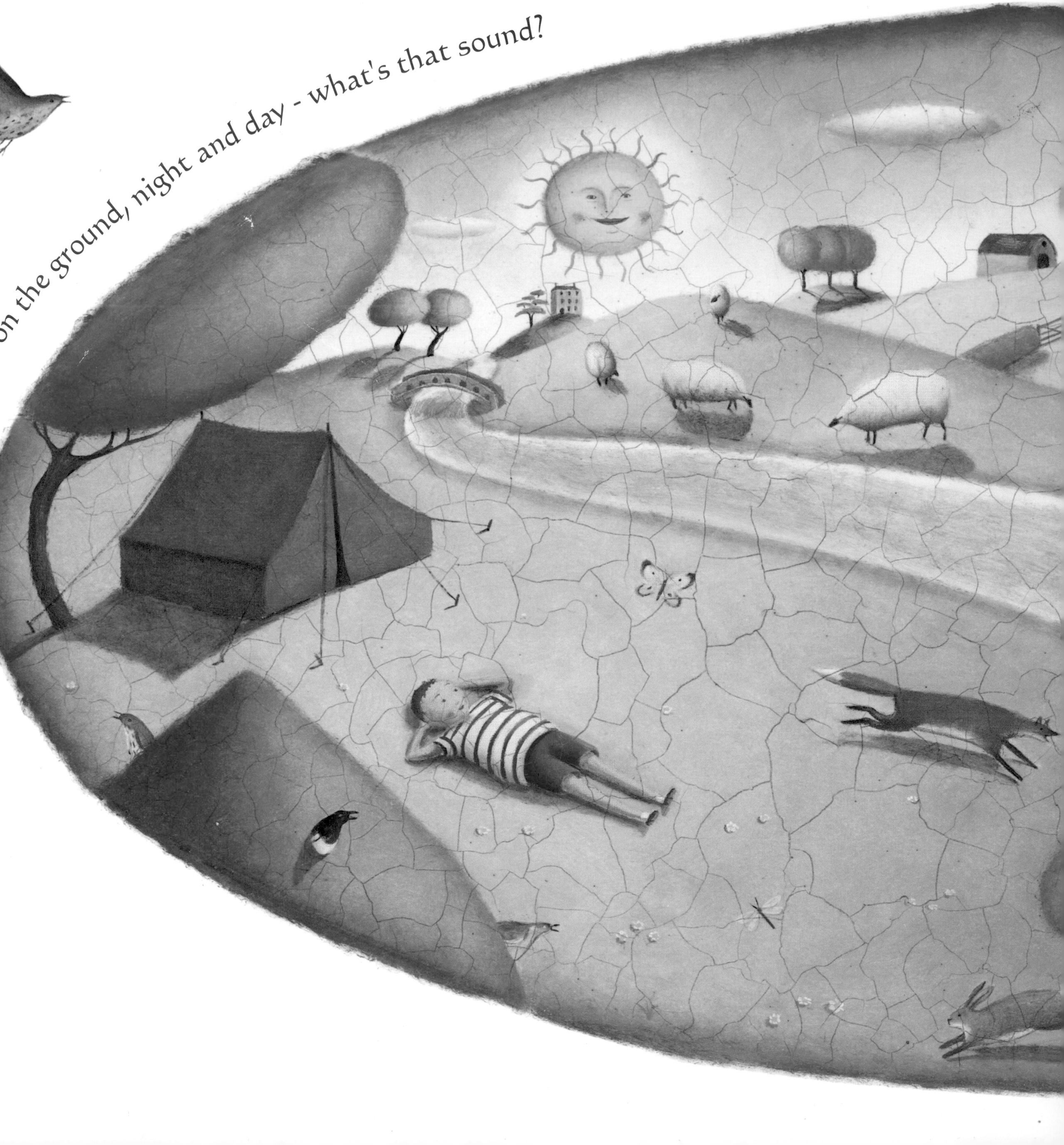

إسمع ، إسمع ... بَعْدَ الربيعِ يحُلُّ فَصلُ الصيفُ و ...

Listen, listen ... after spring, summer comes and ...

تغَنّي الحشراتُ!

Insects sing!

زيِءْ ، زيِءْ ، خِشْ ، زِرّْ ، فِرّْ ، فِرّْ.

Chirp, chirp, churr, churr, buzz, buzz, whirr, whirr.

In the summer, can you see
a cricket
a beetle
a butterfly
a sunflower
a mosquito
a daisy
a dragonfly
a bee
a grasshopper
a leaf?

In the autumn, can you see

an owl

a goose

an acorn

a squirrel

an apple

a stalk of wheat

a pumpkin

an ear of corn

a seagull

a leaf?

In the winter, can you see

a crow

a mouse

a starling

a paw print

an icicle

a holly berry

a leaf?

a snowflake

a sprig of mistletoe

In the spring, can you see
a tulip
a daffodil
a bluebell
a sparrow
a rainbow
a rabbit
a frog
a duckling
a chick
a leaf?

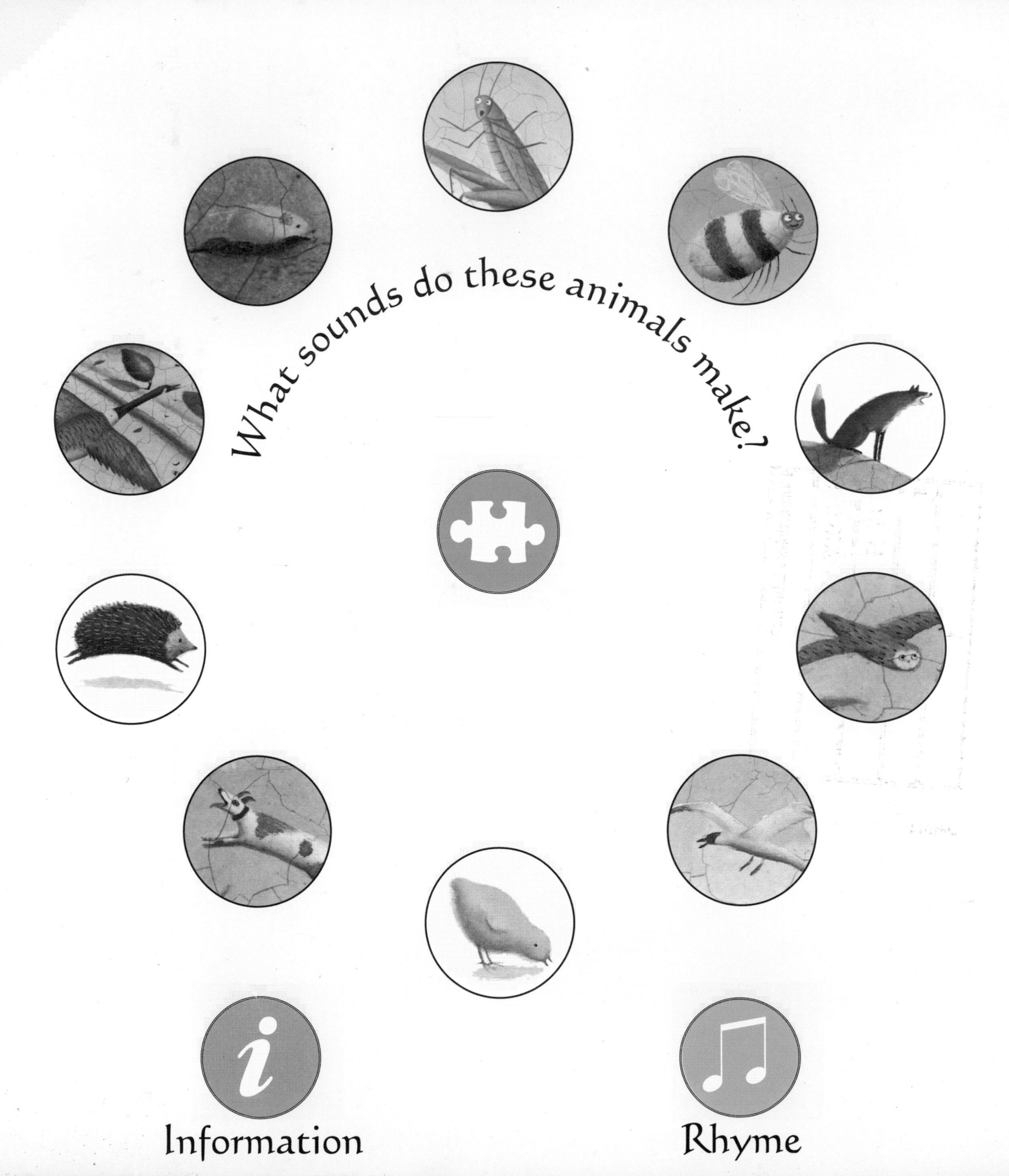
What sounds do these animals make?
Information
Rhyme